TRANSGENDER'S GUIDE TO PHYSICAL TRANSITION WORKBOOK

SAGE BUCH

www.Microcosm.Pub

SKILLS TO CHANGE YOUR LIFE AND THE WORLD

2752 N WILLIAMS AVE · PORTLAND, OR 97277

My Name:

What I Am Most Excited About:

What I Am Most Nervous About:

Why I Got This Workbook:

THE TRANSMASCULINE GUIDE TO PHYSICAL TRANSITION WORKBOOK:
FOR TRANS, NONBINARY, AND OTHER MASCULINE FOLKS

SAGE BUCH

Portland, Ore | Cleveland, Ohio

The Transmasculine Guide to Physical Transition Workbook: For Trans, Nonbinary, and Other Masculine Folks
© Sage Buch, 2023

This edition © Microcosm Publishing, 2023
First Edition, 2,000 copies, First published February, 2023
Design by Joe Biel
Edited by Lydia Rogue
ISBN 9781648411458
This is Microcosm #712

For a catalog, write or visit:
Microcosm Publishing
2752 N Williams Ave.
Portland, OR 97227
(360) 291-7226
For more copies of this book and the accompanying handbook:

www.Microcosm.Pub/TransMasc

Did you know that you can buy our books directly from us at sliding scale rates? Support a small, independent publisher and pay less than Amazon's price at **www.Microcosm.Pub**

To join the ranks of high-class stores that feature Microcosm titles, talk to your rep: In the U.S. **Como** (Atlantic), **Abraham** (Midwest), **Bob Barnett** (Texas/Oklahoma/Louisiana), **Imprint** (Pacific), **Turnaround** in Europe, **Manda/UTP** in Canada, **New South** in Australia, and **GPS** in Asia, India, Africa, and South America. We are sold in the gift market by **Faire**.

Global labor conditions are bad, and our roots in industrial Cleveland in the 70s and 80s made us appreciate the need to treat workers right. Therefore, our books are MADE IN THE USA

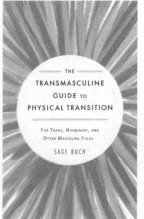

Also available at finer bookstores:
The Transmasculine Guide to Physical Transition
(9781648410727)

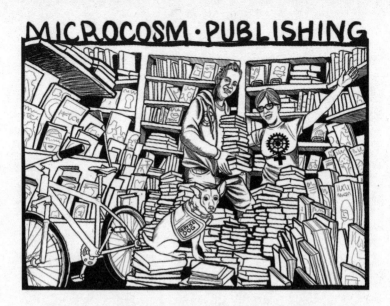

ABOUT THE PUBLISHER

MICROCOSM PUBLISHING is Portland's most diversified publishing house and distributor with a focus on the colorful, authentic, and empowering. Our books and zines have put your power in your hands since 1996, equipping readers to make positive changes in their lives and in the world around them. Microcosm emphasizes skill-building, showing hidden histories, and fostering creativity through challenging conventional publishing wisdom with books and bookettes about DIY skills, food, bicycling, gender, self-care, and social justice. What was once a distro and record label started by Joe Biel in a drafty bedroom was determined to be *Publisher's Weekly's* fastest growing publisher of 2022 and has become among the oldest independent publishing houses in Portland, OR and Cleveland, OH. We are a politically moderate, centrist publisher in a world that has inched to the right for the past 80 years.

PLEASE NOTE:

This workbook was created alongside *The Transmasculine Guide to Physical Transition* by Sage Buch, which provides a comprehensive overview of all currently available options for *physical* transition for transmasculine and nonbinary people. The workbook stands alone and can be used on its own as you explore your options, or together with the guidebook.

This workbook and guidebook do not contain any of the information surrounding *social* transition. This is not because social transition is in any way more or less important, but because there is so much necessary information that needs to be discussed for both physical and social transition that could not feasibly be included without leaving something out.

This book does not contain any information for people who were assigned male at birth (AMAB). This is not because AMAB people cannot be nonbinary, but because I'm not AMAB, and I do not feel confident or competent speaking to those experiences.

AN IMPORTANT LEGAL DISCLAIMER:

I am not a medical professional. I am a transgender person who has personal experience with these topics and who has been reading peer reviewed journals and gathering community knowledge over the last 9 years. Always consult your medical providers, therapists, and surgeons before taking any meaningful steps toward transition. The information in this book is meant to be a general guide and introduction, and to provide helpful information on options for physically transitioning. This book is not meant to be used, nor should it be used, to diagnose or treat any medical condition. This book is not intended as a substitute for consultation with a licensed healthcare professional, such as your PCP, therapist, or surgeon. Before you begin or change any healthcare program, hormone treatment, or change part of your lifestyle in any way, you should consult your physician or other licensed healthcare professional to ensure that you are in good health and that the examples contained in this book will not harm you. The publisher and author are not responsible for any specific health or allergy needs that may require medical supervision and are not liable for any damages or negative consequences from any treatment, action, application, or preparation, to any person reading or following the information in this book. References are provided for informational purposes only and do not constitute endorsement of any websites or other sources. Readers should be aware that the websites listed in this book may change. This book provides content related to physical and mental health issues; as such, use of this book implies your acceptance of this disclaimer.

CONTENTS

Checking in With Yourself • 10

Binding • 16

Packing • 20

Hormone Replacement Therapy • 24

Top Surgery • 29

Bottom Surgery • 55

Meta • 76
Phallo • 86

Resources • 102

Conclusion • 107

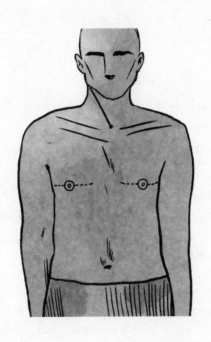

CHECKING IN WITH YOURSELF

How do you begin your journey when it comes to physically transitioning?

The most important thing is constantly checking in with yourself, which is something we'll be doing a lot of in this book. It's important to figure out your wants, needs, desires, and what is important to you. Before you start, let's first remind ourselves of a few things:

1) You do not need to physically transition to be your gender.

2) You do not need to physically transition to please anyone but yourself.

3) You do not need to physically transition to "prove" anything.

4) You do not need to physically transition to be trans.

5) No matter what options you want or need, they do not invalidate your gender.

Something that you'll do a lot of in this workbook is check in with yourself to see what *you* want and need. When it comes to changing and altering your physical self, it's important to determine what is right for you and what meets your needs. It is the unfortunate truth that, as a trans person, you may feel pressure from medical and mental providers, family, and even friends to transition in the way that they think determines your gender, or seems right to them. No matter other people's feelings, it's important to check in with yourself about what makes *you* happy and fulfilled, regardless of what anyone else says.

Questions for Reflection

Let's take some time to first reflect within, and write out our thoughts, feelings, and emotions surrounding physical transition:

How do I see my body, and how would I like that to be reflected to the outside world?

From that, what changes, if any, do I hope to make?

What steps have I already taken?

What steps do I hope to take, and on what timeline?

What am I most excited about?

What am I most nervous about?

Where do I see myself in one year?

Where do I see myself in five years?

Where do I see myself in twenty years?

What questions do I have?

Any additional thoughts:

BINDING

Chest binding is the action of wearing something to make your chest appear flat. There are a number of different ways that you can safely bind, and there are many ways out there that are not safe and may cause long term damage.

Do not use elastic bandages (like ACE bandages), duct tape, binders that are too small, or multiple binders at once. Safer options are well-fitting binders, sports bras, and TransTape.

Placement of your chest under the binder depends both on personal preference as well as the instructions of the manufacturer (if there are any instructions). Most people either have their chest tissue facing forward or pulled slightly to the sides. While it may be tempting, don't shove the tissue uncomfortably far out or down. Over time, this can be really painful and will add to any loss of skin elasticity from wearing your binder. Keep in mind, the binder is most effective when you're the most comfortable in it. If you have a binder that you never want to wear because you're uncomfortable, it will not be effective. Check out the Binders chapter in *The Transmasculine Guide to Physical Transition* for more in-depth discussion of safer binding.

What is my budget for a binder?

Does it matter whether my binder is visible to other people?

What are my options with the size of my chest?

Is my chest small enough for TransTape? If so, is this an option I would want to use?

Do I have a preference of full vs half tank binders? Why or why not?

Does it matter to me what kind of compression the binder has?

Do I have any injuries or aspects of my health that may prevent me from using a binder?

Do I want a binder that will also compress my stomach and hips?

Does the color of my binder matter? If so, what color?

Does how discreet the binder looks matter to me?

Do I know anyone who has a binder I can try first before buying one?

Are there any other thoughts or feelings I have around binding?

Brand	Price	Where to Buy	Sizing Options	Notes

What else is on my mind?

PACKING

Similar to binding, but for your lower half, packing is the aspect of wearing (packing) something in your pants to have a bulge. For some people, this may mean using something that allows them to stand to pee, for others, this may mean just having something there in order to feel more comfortable and at home in their bodies and how they look.

What is my budget for packers?

How important is cost?

What is most important to me with packing? (i.e. peeing, playing, the bulge shape, etc)

Is being able to pee standing up, or at a urinal important to me?

Does how well the STP would "pass" matter to me?

Is being able to play without switching over to a strap-on important to me?

Does it matter if the packer is "realistic"?

Does it matter if the packer creates a traditional bulge?

Does it matter if the packer passes the "grab test"?

Do I have any bottom growth (or lack thereof) that may interfere with the way certain packers work?

Does it matter to me if the packer is "body-safe"?

Could I budget for a body-safe packer?

What am I comfortable with, size-wise?

Do I want a particular color, or skin tone to my packer?

Brand	Price	Where to Buy	Sizing Options	Notes

What else is on my mind?

HORMONE REPLACEMENT THERAPY

HRT (hormone replacement therapy) is a medical treatment through which you manually deliver testosterone (or, for trans-feminine people: estrogen, progesterone, and androgen blockers) to supplement or change your body's dominant hormone. You may also see this described as "T," "hormones," "mones," or other community terms such as "anti-cis-tamines" or "boy juice." I will primarily use the letter "T" as a shorthand. Testosterone is considered a "masculinizing" hormone and has a number of both reversible and irreversible effects. Side effects that are reversible would stop and change back to how they were pre-HRT if you were to stop taking T. Irreversible changes would remain, even if you decide to cease hormone use in the future.

Irreversible Effects

Effects	Expected Onset	Expected Maximum Effect
Bottom Growth	1-6 Months	1-2 Years
Deepened Voice	3-6 Months	1-2 Years
Facial/ Body Hair Growth	3-6 Months	3-5 Years
Scalp Hair Loss	>12 Months	Variable

Reversible Effects

Effect	Expected Onset	Expected Maximum Effect
Increased Libido	0-2 Months	Unknown
Increased Energy Levels	1-6 Months	1-2 Years
Skin Oiliness/ Acne	1-6 Months	1-2 Years
Skin Thickness/ Roughness	3-6 Months	1-2 Years

Body Fat Redistribution	3-6 Months	2-5 Years
Increased Muscle Mass	3-6 Months	2-5 Years
Cessation of Menses	2-6 months	N/A
Vaginal Atrophy	3-6 Months	1-2 Years

HRT Check-in

What changes am I excited about?

What changes am I ambivalent about?

What changes am I nervous about, or may make me dysphoric?

If I start to pass as male, how will I feel?

If I'm on testosterone for a while and don't pass as male, how will I feel?

Do I want to be on a low dose?

Do I eventually want to work up to a "full" dose?

Am I comfortable doing shots myself, or should I get a form of T that I do not self inject?

Am I comfortable coming out to family/friends/work (if I'm not already) as changes become more noticeable?

Are there any other thoughts or feelings that I'm having about HRT?

Use this table to make a pros and cons list, and assign a number, somewhere between 1 and 5, to each thought. 1 means it isn't a huge deal, 3 means it matters somewhat to you, and 5 means being that it's a big deal. At the end, add them all up, and see which value is higher.

Pros	Value 1-5	Value 1-5	Cons
Total Pros			**Total Cons**

What are my overall thoughts after going through these questions, and the Pros and Cons list?

What are my overall thoughts after going through this chapter?

What else is on my mind?

TOP SURGERY

Top surgery refers to any surgery performed on your chest to reduce or remove chest tissue. There are many different kinds: those that leave noticeable scars, those that don't, those that retain some nipple sensation, those that don't, those that leave some tissue or size behind, and those that remove everything.

Surgeries that Leave Noticeable Scars

Surgery Type	Who Is Eligible?	Retain Nipple Sensitivity?
Double Incision **(2 Scars)**	Almost Everybody If you have a lot of tissue in the center of your chest, or your chest meets in the middle, you may require a connected scar	No
Double Incision **(1 scar)**	Almost Everybody If your chest is very small, this may not be possible.	No
Buttonhole	People who measure 3 in (8cm)* or less from the inframammary fold** to the nipple	Some***
Inverted-T	People who measure 3 in (8cm) or less from the inframammary fold to the nipple	Some
Fishmouth	People who measure 3 in (8cm) or less from the inframammary fold to the nipple	Some

*8cm is a conservative estimate, and some surgeons will allow up to 4 in (11cm). Always check with your surgeon to see what measurements they recommend and are comfortable with.

**The "inframammary fold" is where chest tissue "folds over" on the underside (where the band of a sports bra usually rests). So this is a measurement from your chest wall, along the slope of the tissue coming from it, to your nipple.

***I say "some" here because, while the nipple sensation is retained in theory, many people report only having a fraction of the sensation they used to have, and sometimes losing sensation altogether.

Surgeries that do not leave noticeable scars

Surgery Type	Who is Eligible?	Retain Nipple Sensitivity?
Keyhole	People who have very small chests (small A cup or smaller) Nipples are already relatively in a "male placement" (not too low) Areola is relatively small Good skin elasticity	Some
Periareolar (Peri)	People who have smaller chests (A or small B cup) Nipples are already in a relatively "male placement" (not too low) Good skin elasticity	Some

What surgery types am I eligible for?

Circle yes or no:

Double Incision:	Yes	No
Buttonhole:	Yes	No
Inverted T:	Yes	No
Fishmouth:	Yes	No
Keyhole:	Yes	No
Periareolar:	Yes	No

Do I want to be completely flat, or have a radical reduction?

Is nipple sensitivity important to me?

What do I want my scar shape to look like?

Do I want to have nipples?

What other thoughts or concerns do I have with top surgery?

Draw your Ideal Chest!

Include: What kind of incisions you want, where your nipples would go (if you want them), and add any body art as you see fit!

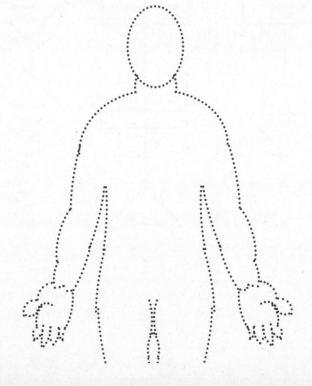

Top Surgery Decision Flow Chart

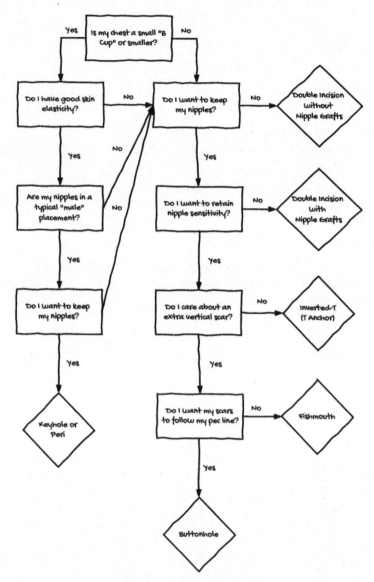

Top Surgery

Questions About Potential Surgeons

How important is it that a surgeon takes my insurance?

Does it matter how close a surgeon is to where I live?

Does it matter to me how much surgery costs?

Does it matter if a surgeon requires me to be on testosterone?

Does it matter to me if a surgeon requires letters from a therapist vs. if they operate on informed consent?

Does it matter if the surgeon has a BMI requirement?

Does it matter if they have experience performing surgery on people with my BMI?

Does it matter if they have experience performing surgery on people with my skin color/tone?

Does it matter if they use drains or not?

Surgeon Research

Surgeon #1:

Location:

Cost for Surgery: Cost for Travel:

Do they take my insurance? (circle one)   Yes No

Do they do the procedure I want? (circle one)   Yes No

Do they have a BMI Requirement? (circle one)   Yes No

Do they operate on informed consent, or require a therapist's letter?

Do they have experience with people with my BMI and skin tone/color?

What is the community reputation of this surgeon?

What are my overall feelings about this surgeon?

Surgeon #2:

Location:

Cost for Surgery: Cost for Travel:

Do they take my insurance? (circle one)   Yes No

Do they do the procedure I want? (circle one)   Yes No

Do they have a BMI Requirement? (circle one)   Yes No

Do they operate on informed consent, or require a therapist's letter?

Do they have experience with people with my BMI and skin tone/color?

What is the community reputation of this surgeon?

What are my overall feelings about this surgeon?

Surgeon #3:

Location:

Cost for Surgery: Cost for Travel:

Do they take my insurance? (circle one)   Yes No

Do they do the procedure I want? (circle one)   Yes No

Do they have a BMI Requirement? (circle one)   Yes No

Do they operate on informed consent, or require a therapist's letter?

Do they have experience with people with my BMI and skin tone/color?

What is the community reputation of this surgeon?

What are my overall feelings about this surgeon?

Surgeon #4:

Location:

Cost for Surgery: Cost for Travel:

Do they take my insurance? (circle one)   Yes No

Do they do the procedure I want? (circle one)   Yes No

Do they have a BMI Requirement? (circle one)   Yes No

Do they operate on informed consent, or require a therapist's letter?

Do they have experience with people with my BMI and skin tone/color?

What is the community reputation of this surgeon?

What are my overall feelings about this surgeon?

Surgeon #5:

Location:

Cost for Surgery: Cost for Travel:

Do they take my insurance? (circle one)   Yes No

Do they do the procedure I want? (circle one)   Yes No

Do they have a BMI Requirement? (circle one)   Yes No

Do they operate on informed consent, or require a therapist's letter?

Do they have experience with people with my BMI and skin tone/color?

What is the community reputation of this surgeon?

What are my overall feelings about this surgeon?

Surgeon Consultations

Hot Tip! If virtual, ask your surgeon if you can record your consultation so that you can go back and listen to/ watch it when you are making decisions.

Surgeon #1:

Location: Date:

How many of these surgeries do you perform every year?

How many of these surgeries have you performed total?

I want _____ procedure, is this a procedure you regularly perform?

Is this a procedure you're comfortable performing on a person with my body type?

What percentage of your patients have had severe complications?

How many of your patients come back for revisions?

Are revisions included in the initial cost?

Do you have experience doing surgery on people with my skin tone or color?

Do you have any legal cases pending against you from other trans patients?

Notes:

Surgeon #2:

Location: Date:

How many of these surgeries do you perform every year?

How many of these surgeries have you performed total?

I want _____ procedure, is this a procedure you regularly perform?

Is this a procedure you're comfortable performing on a person with my body type?

What percentage of your patients have had severe complications?

How many of your patients come back for revisions?

Are revisions included in the initial cost?

Do you have experience doing surgery on people with my skin tone or color?

Do you have any legal cases pending against you from other trans patients?

Notes:

Surgeon #3:

Location: Date:

How many of these surgeries do you perform every year?

How many of these surgeries have you performed total?

I want _____ procedure, is this a procedure you regularly perform?

Is this a procedure you're comfortable performing on a person with my body type?

What percentage of your patients have had severe complications?

How many of your patients come back for revisions?

Are revisions included in the initial cost?

Do you have experience doing surgery on people with my skin tone or color?

Do you have any legal cases pending against you from other trans patients?

Notes:

Surgeon #4:

Location: Date:

How many of these surgeries do you perform every year?

How many of these surgeries have you performed total?

I want _____ procedure, is this a procedure you regularly perform?

Is this a procedure you're comfortable performing on a person with my body type?

What percentage of your patients have had severe complications?

How many of your patients come back for revisions?

Are revisions included in the initial cost?

Do you have experience doing surgery on people with my skin tone or color?

Do you have any legal cases pending against you from other trans patients?

Notes:

Surgeon #5:

Location: Date:

How many of these surgeries do you perform every year?

How many of these surgeries have you performed total?

I want _____ procedure, is this a procedure you regularly perform?

Is this a procedure you're comfortable performing on a person with my body type?

What percentage of your patients have had severe complications?

How many of your patients come back for revisions?

Are revisions included in the initial cost?

Do you have experience doing surgery on people with my skin tone or color?

Do you have any legal cases pending against you from other trans patients?

Notes:

Surgery Info Worksheet

Once you've chosen a surgeon and made an appointment, use this worksheet to plan.

Surgeon:

Location: Date:

Name and phone number of person who will pick me up after surgery:

Name of person who will care for me during the first 48 hours after surgery:

Time off work arrangements:

Insurance/financial arrangements:

Travel plans:

Housing address and info:

Pre-op appointment information:

Post-op appointment information:

Additional Surgery Notes

Shopping List

Clothing

- ◯ Comfy, loose, front button shirts
- ◯ Comfy, loose zip up jackets/ sweatshirts
- ◯ Comfy, loose pull on pants/shorts
- ◯ Socks (including compression socks)
- ◯ Underwear
- ◯ Slip-on shoes

First Aid Kit

- ◯ Large gauze pads
- ◯ Small gauze pads
- ◯ Paper medical tape
- ◯ Bacitracin
- ◯ Alcohol prep pads
- ◯ Extra-strength Tylenol (Or whatever over-the-counter painkiller your doctor recommends)

- ☐ Elastic bandage or post-op binder
- ☐ Baby wipes / body wipes
- ☐ Any necessary medications
- ☐ Stool softener
- ☐ Laxative
- ☐ Throat coat tea / cough drops
- ☐ Arnica and bromelain (if your surgeon recommends)

General Comfort

- ☐ Blanket from home
- ☐ Extra-long phone cord
- ☐ Extra pillows
- ☐ Spare pillowcase
- ☐ Neck pillow or wedge pillow
- ☐ Bendy straw
- ☐ Dry shampoo
- ☐ Cash/mobile app for ordering food
- ☐ Whatever you need to keep your mind entertained (Books, video games, music, computer, crafts, etc)

Food

- ☐ Fruits (Pineapple and Blueberries both contain high levels of bromelain)
- ☐ Vegetables
- ☐ Whole grains
- ☐ Lean protein (chicken or lentils are a great choice)

- [ ] Soup
- [ ] Smoothie ingredients
- [ ] Food that you'll eat on an upset stomach
- [ ] Water
- [ ] Ginger Ale or ginger tea (to help with an upset stomach)

Additional Items

- [ ]
- [ ]
- [ ]
- [ ]
- [ ]
- [ ]

Top Surgery Timeline

The week before surgery

Dates _____

- [ ] Gather any post-op supplies you will need and pack.

- [ ] Prepare your home so that anything you need will be in reach of your "T-Rex arms" post op (you will not be allowed to reach above your head for 6-8 weeks).

- [ ] If you are traveling to your surgeon, try to arrive a day before required, so your surgery is not potentially impacted or canceled by travel delays.

- [ ] Attend a pre-op appointment, where they check in with you to make sure everything is okay, give you your medication scripts to fill, and go over what will happen the day of and a few days after surgery. It's different for every surgeon, so be sure to follow what your surgeon states.

The day before surgery

Date

◯ Complete any final preparations you were not able to get to in the couple of days before.

◯ Take out any of your metal jewelry, as you cannot wear metal of any kind during surgery. You can replace the metal jewelry with silicone or plastic jewelry, or with hole holders, so that the holes don't close.

◯ If you have nipple piercings, ask your surgeon for specific guidelines on what they'd like you to do pre-op, and be sure to follow these. Note that you may need to get your nipples repierced after surgery if you'd like to keep nipple piercings. It is generally recommended to wait six months to a year post-op before piercing your nipple grafts, but you should follow the recommendations of your surgeon.

◯ Your surgeon may request that you shower with a chlorhexidine skin cleanser, the same type the surgeon uses to wash their hands before an operation, the night before. These can be found at most local pharmacies under the brand name "Hibiclens", and they will give you instructions on how to use it.

The day of surgery, pre-op:

Date

◯ Do not eat or drink anything from midnight until after surgery

◯ Arrive at the surgery center, fill out any forms or necessary payment

You will then be called to the back, where your surgeon and nurses will prep you for surgery.

This usually includes getting into a hospital gown and hooking you up to saline and monitors.

Your surgeon will later come in and have you sit or stand up straight and will then draw on your chest where the incisions will be, and check in with you to see how you're feeling.

Your anesthesiologist will come in and begin to set up and potentially start some of the anesthesia, and your surgical team will wheel you back to the operating room.

The day of surgery, post-op:

Date

When you wake up, you'll be in a recovery room with nurses who will bring you something to drink and potentially some easy-to-digest food like graham crackers. You'll likely be groggy, and your chest will be bound in bandages with a post-op binder or elastic bandage wrapping them to you. If your surgeon uses bulb drains, these will be visible. These are not removed until the post-op appointment around 7 days post-op.

Eventually, whoever is there for your recovery will be brought in to talk to you and bring you home. You likely won't remember this part, but they will also be trained in how to care for your drains if you have them, be given your medicine schedule, and given any warning signs that they should call the surgeon's office about. Most of the time, top surgery is an outpatient procedure, though if there are additional health concerns that your surgeon wants to mitigate, they may keep you in the hospital for a day or two.

The first 48 hours:

Dates

◯ It is mandatory that someone is with you for the first 48 hours after surgery to care for you, be responsible for your meds, or bring you back to the hospital if there are any severe complications (which can happen for any surgery).

◯ Do not lift anything more than 5 pounds

◯ Do not remove the binder and bandages, or get them wet

◯ You will have a limited range of motion, fondly called "t-rex arms" in the community.

The first week:

Dates

◯ Continue to not lift anything more than 5 pounds.

◯ Continue to stick to "t-rex arms".

◯ Follow your surgeon's guidelines on binder removal and showering

- *Most require you to wait until after the drains are removed, but shower allowance and bandage removal may differ if your surgeon does not use drains.*

- *If you're feeling stinky or dirty, gently "bathe" yourself with wet wipes, being sure not to get the wipes close to anything that you shouldn't get wet.*

◯ Begin periodically taking short walks to keep up your circulation.

◯ It is expected that you won't be able to be very active and will tire easily. Be sure to give yourself the space you need to heal and rest as much as you need. You will spend most of this first week slowly recovering, drinking lots of water, and doing your best to keep your mind active.

◯ Following the first week, the surgeon will usually take out your drains (if they use them), and you will see your chest.

The first post-op appointment:

Dates

◯ This is generally when your bandages and drains are removed, and you get to see your chest for the first time! Drain removal sounds a lot worse than it is. You may feel a pinching sensation when they're removed, but for many people it is painless.

◯ If you have any buildup of fluid in your chest that was too viscous for the drains to remove, your surgeon will get this out. This generally occurs by them gently pushing the fluid towards the drain hole until it comes out. Many people describe this as a "grape jelly" consistency, and say it's not really uncomfortable, but if you're squeamish, to look away.

◯ If you haven't been allowed to yet, you are now allowed to shower that day or the next. Make sure not to face the shower, because this can damage your incisions and/or your nipples, if you have them.

The next 3 weeks:
Dates

○ At this point, you are generally allowed to lift things that weigh as much as a gallon of milk or less.

○ Shower daily, apply dressings to your nipples and drain holes, if you have them, and continue to wear your compression vest or elastic bandage. Your surgeon should give you instructions to care for both.

Drain Output

Date	Time	Color	Amount

Track Your Meds

Medication Name	Sunday AM	Sunday PM	Sunday Bed	Monday AM	Monday PM	Monday Bed	Tuesday AM	Tuesday PM	Tuesday Bed	Wednes-day AM	Wednes-day PM	Wednes-day Bed	Thurs-day AM	Thurs-day PM	Thurs-day Bed	Friday AM	Friday AM	Friday Bed	Saturday AM	Saturday PM	Saturday Bed

A letter to your post-op self

Sometimes after surgery, folks are hit with post-op depression, a tough mental place where they may question their decision or feel generally depressed. It comes from a variety of places, like having to limit your behavior, having complications, needing to have other people care for you, or your body having gone through trauma (no matter how necessary and important that trauma is). Use this space to write to your post-surgery self, as something you can read if you end up in that place. Some things you could write are: how important this is to you, to remember to take it slow, honoring your healing process, knowing how much better your life will be post-op, or whatever else feels right!

BOTTOM SURGERY

Bottom surgery is the overarching term for a number of surgeries that can be performed to either make the current tdick (what cisgender people would call the clitoris) more prominent, give the ability to stand to pee, create a scrotum, create a cis-male sized penis, remove the vagina to create a perinium, or more.

Metoidioplasty ("Meta"): Releasing the tdick from any ligaments or body structure holding it down.

Phalloplasty ("Phallo"): Creating a cis-male sized phallus (neophallus / new dick) from a donor site.

Urethral Lengthening (UL): Extending the urethra to pee through the tdick or neophallus.

Scrotoplasty ("Scroto"): Creation of the balls/ ballsack.

Vaginectomy ("V-nectomy"): Closure of the vagina / front hole to create a perineum (removal of reproductive organs is required).

Nerve Hookup: Attaching a nerve (or nerves) from your tdick to a nerve (or nerves) in your neophallus to transfer erotic sensation.

Phalloplasty Options

Donor Site	Requirements	Is Nerve Hookup Possible?
Forearm (RFF)	None	Yes
Thigh (ALT)	Passes the "Pinch Test"	Yes
Back (MLD)	None	Possible, though rarely done
Abdominal Flap	None	No

Is the ability to have and use my front hole important to me?

Is getting rid of my front hole important to me?

Does the ability to have biological children in the future matter to me?

Is freezing eggs important to me?

Do the potential complications from v-nectomy make it worth it to me?

Is having (or not having) my front hole the most important part for me?

Is the ability to stand to pee important to me?

Is the ability to stand to pee worth the potential complications for me?

Is the ability to stand to pee the most important part for me?

Is it important to be able to keep my front hole and to be able to stand to pee?

Is having a scrotum important to me?

Is having balls important to me, or just the scrotal sac?

If having balls is important to me does the size of them matter to me?

Is having (or not having) a scrotum the most important part to me?

Does it matter to me if my genitals look like a cisgender man's?

Does it matter if I'll be able to penetrate a partner?

Does it matter to me if I'm able to "jerk off" in a way resembling a cis man?

Does it matter to me how many surgical procedures/stages I'll need?

Does it matter if I'm able to get erections?

Does it matter If I'm able to get assisted or unassisted erections?

Does size matter to me?

If I decide on phallo, does erogenous sensation matter to me?

If I decide on phallo, does nerve hookup matter to me?

If I decide on phallo, does scar placement / donor site matter to me?

If I decide on phallo, does type of erection device matter to me?

If I decide on phallo, does burying, or not burying, my tdick matter to me?

Does my insurance cover bottom surgery? If not, does it matter to me if my insurance doesn't cover bottom surgery?

Could I get insurance that covers bottom surgery?

What other thoughts and feelings am I having about bottom surgery?

Surgeon Research

Surgeon #1:   Location:

Cost for Surgery: Cost for Travel:

Do they take my insurance? (circle one)   Yes No

Do they do the procedure I want? (circle one)   Yes No

Do they have a BMI Requirement? (circle one)   Yes No

Do they operate on informed consent, or require a therapist's letter?

Do they have experience with people with my BMI and skin tone/color?

What is this surgeon's reputation in the community?

What are my overall feelings about this surgeon?

Surgeon #2:   Location:

Cost for Surgery: Cost for Travel:

Do they take my insurance? (circle one)   Yes No

Do they do the procedure I want? (circle one)   Yes No

Do they have a BMI Requirement? (circle one)   Yes No

Do they operate on informed consent, or require a therapist's letter?

Do they have experience with people with my BMI and skin tone/color?

What is this surgeon's reputation in the community?

What are my overall feelings about this surgeon?

Surgeon #3:   Location:

Cost for Surgery: Cost for Travel:

Do they take my insurance? (circle one)   Yes No

Do they do the procedure I want? (circle one)   Yes No

Do they have a BMI Requirement? (circle one)   Yes No

Do they operate on informed consent, or require a therapist's letter?

Do they have experience with people with my BMI and skin tone/color?

What is this surgeon's reputation in the community?

What are my overall feelings about this surgeon?

Surgeon #4:   Location:

Cost for Surgery: Cost for Travel:

Do they take my insurance? (circle one)   Yes   No

Do they do the procedure I want? (circle one)   Yes   No

Do they have a BMI Requirement? (circle one)   Yes   No

Do they operate on informed consent, or require a therapist's letter?

Do they have experience with people with my BMI and skin tone/color?

What is this surgeon's reputation in the community?

What are my overall feelings about this surgeon?

Surgeon #5:   Location:

Cost for Surgery: Cost for Travel:

Do they take my insurance? (circle one)   Yes   No

Do they do the procedure I want? (circle one)   Yes   No

Do they have a BMI Requirement? (circle one)   Yes   No

Do they operate on informed consent, or require a therapist's letter?

Do they have experience with people with my BMI and skin tone/color?

What is this surgeon's reputation in the community?

What are my overall feelings about this surgeon?

Surgeon Consultations

Hot Tip! If virtual, ask you surgeon if you can record your consultation so you can go back and listen to/ watch it when you are making decisions.

Surgeon #1:

Location: Date:

How many of these surgeries do you perform every year?

How many of these surgeries have you performed total?

Where did you receive training for phalloplasty/metoidioplasty?

I want _____ procedure, is this a procedure you regularly perform?

Is this a procedure you're comfortable performing on a person with my body type?

How many stages would you do this procedure in?

What is your complication rate with UL?

What percentage of your patients have had severe complications?

How many of your patients come back for revisions?

Are revisions included in the initial cost? (These are not stages; a revision is to modify something already done)

Do you have experience doing surgery on people with my skin tone or color?

Do you have experience doing UL with people who keloid?

Do you have any legal cases pending against you from other trans patients?

If having phallo:

What is your success rate with nerve hookup?

I want ___ donor site, is this something you're comfortable performing with my body type?

How many nerves do you hook up?

If they use both tdick nerves, rather than an "ilioinguinal" nerve and a tdick nerve:

What percentage of people you've performed this surgery on have completely lost sensation?

Notes:

Surgeon #2:

Location: Date:

How many of these surgeries do you perform every year?

How many of these surgeries have you performed total?

Where did you receive training for phalloplasty/metoidioplasty?

I want _____ procedure, is this a procedure you regularly perform?

Is this a procedure you're comfortable performing on a person with my body type?

How many stages would you do this procedure in?

What is your complication rate with UL?

What percentage of your patients have had severe complications?

How many of your patients come back for revisions?

Are revisions included in the initial cost? (These are not stages; a revision is to modify something already done)

Do you have experience doing surgery on people with my skin tone or color?

Do you have experience doing UL with people who keloid?

Do you have any legal cases pending against you from other trans patients?

If having phallo:

What is your success rate with nerve hookup?

I want ___ donor site, is this something you're comfortable performing with my body type?

How many nerves do you hook up?

If they use both tdick nerves, rather than an "ilioinguinal" nerve and a tdick nerve:

What percentage of people you've performed this surgery on have completely lost sensation?

Notes:

Surgeon #3:

Location: Date:

How many of these surgeries do you perform every year?

How many of these surgeries have you performed total?

Where did you receive training for phalloplasty/metoidioplasty?

I want _____ procedure, is this a procedure you regularly perform?

Is this a procedure you're comfortable performing on a person with my body type?

How many stages would you do this procedure in?

What is your complication rate with UL?

What percentage of your patients have had severe complications?

How many of your patients come back for revisions?

Are revisions included in the initial cost? (These are not stages; a revision is to modify something already done)

Do you have experience doing surgery on people with my skin tone or color?

Do you have experience doing UL with people who keloid?

Do you have any legal cases pending against you from other trans patients?

If having phallo:

What is your success rate with nerve hookup?

I want ____ donor site, is this something you're comfortable performing with my body type?

How many nerves do you hook up?

If they use both tdick nerves, rather than an "ilioinguinal" nerve and a tdick nerve:

What percentage of people you've performed this surgery on have completely lost sensation?

Notes:

Surgeon #4:

Location: _____   Date: _____

How many of these surgeries do you perform every year?

How many of these surgeries have you performed total?

Where did you receive training for phalloplasty/metoidioplasty?

I want _____ procedure, is this a procedure you regularly perform?

Is this a procedure you're comfortable performing on a person with my body type?

How many stages would you do this procedure in?

What is your complication rate with UL?

What percentage of your patients have had severe complications?

How many of your patients come back for revisions?

Are revisions included in the initial cost? (These are not stages; a revision is to modify something already done)

Do you have experience doing surgery on people with my skin tone or color?

Do you have experience doing UL with people who keloid?

Do you have any legal cases pending against you from other trans patients?

If having phallo:

What is your success rate with nerve hookup?

I want _____ donor site, is this something you're comfortable performing with my body type?

How many nerves do you hook up?

If they use both tdick nerves, rather than an "ilioinguinal" nerve and a tdick nerve:

What percentage of people you've performed this surgery on have completely lost sensation?

Notes:

Surgeon #5:

Location: Date:

How many of these surgeries do you perform every year?

How many of these surgeries have you performed total?

Where did you receive training for phalloplasty/metoidioplasty?

I want ＿＿＿ procedure, is this a procedure you regularly perform?

Is this a procedure you're comfortable performing on a person with my body type?

How many stages would you do this procedure in?

What is your complication rate with UL?

What percentage of your patients have had severe complications?

How many of your patients come back for revisions?

Are revisions included in the initial cost? (These are not stages; a revision is to modify something already done)

Do you have experience doing surgery on people with my skin tone or color?

Do you have experience doing UL with people who keloid?

Do you have any legal cases pending against you from other trans patients?

If having phallo:

What is your success rate with nerve hookup?

I want ＿＿＿ donor site, is this something you're comfortable performing with my body type?

How many nerves do you hook up?

If they use both tdick nerves, rather than an "ilioinguinal" nerve and a tdick nerve:

What percentage of people you've performed this surgery on have completely lost sensation?

Notes:

Surgery Info Worksheet

Once you've chosen a surgeon and made an appointment, use this worksheet to plan.

Surgeon:

Location: Date:

Name and phone number of person who will pick me up after surgery:

Name of person who will care for me during the first two weeks after surgery:

Time off work arrangements:

Insurance/financial arrangements:

Travel plans:

Housing address and info:

Pre-op appointment information:

Post-op appointment information:

Shopping List

Clothing

◯ Comfy shirts and jackets

◯ Comfy, loose, pull on pants/shorts (preferably dark colors in case you bleed on them)

◯ Mesh underwear

◯ Socks (including compression socks)

◯ Any additional underwear

◯ Slip-on shoes

First Aid Kit

◯ Exam gloves

◯ Q-tips / cotton balls

◯ Medi-honey

◯ Bacitracin

◯ Alcohol prep pads

◯ Gauze rolls

◯ Xeroform/Adaptic Gauze

◯ Paper medical tape

◯ Sharp scissors

◯ Any necessary medications

◯ Stool softener

◯ Laxative

◯ Throat coat tea / cough drops

◯ Arnica and bromelain (if your doctor recommends)

◯ Additional recommendations from your surgeon:

◯

◯

◯

◯

General Comfort

- ☐ Hand mirror (to check things out after surgery)
- ☐ Extra-long phone cord
- ☐ Donut pillow to sit on
- ☐ Waterproof sheet/ bed pad for wherever you lay post-op
- ☐ Dark sheets you're comfortable bleeding on
- ☐ Dry shampoo
- ☐ Cash/mobile app for ordering food
- ☐ Whatever you need to keep your mind entertained (Books, video games, music, computer, crafts, etc)
- ☐ Blankets from home that help you feel loved and comfortable

Food

- ☐ Fruits (Pineapple and Blueberries both contain high levels of bromelain)
- ☐ Vegetables
- ☐ Whole grains
- ☐ Lean protein (chicken or lentils are a great choice)
- ☐ Soup
- ☐ Smoothie ingredients
- ☐ Food that you'll eat on an upset stomach
- ☐ Water
- ☐ Ginger Ale or ginger tea (to help with an upset stomach)

Additional Items

- ☐
- ☐
- ☐
- ☐
- ☐

Meta Timeline

6 months pre-op

Date

◯ If you are getting a vaginectomy, you are required to have your reproductive organs removed 4-6 months before meta. It is rare that a surgeon will allow these to be done in the same operation, as they are both complex procedures and can cause bleeding in similar areas. (If you are not having a v-nectomy, some surgeons will do both meta and the removal of reproductive organs at the same time).

◯ Make your travel plans, complete any preparations that your surgeon may require of you.

The week before surgery

Dates

◯ Gather any post-op supplies you will need and pack.

◯ Prepare your house/apartment so that anything you need will be on the first floor. Climbing stairs is very uncomfortable, and may not be possible in the first few days post-op.

◯ If you are traveling to your surgeon, try to arrive a day before required, so your surgery is not potentially impacted or canceled by travel delays. Some surgeons may require an in-person pre-op appointment a day or two before your surgery, so ensure you're there in time for that, should they have one.

◯ Attend a pre-op appointment, where they check in with you to make sure everything is good to go, give you your medication scripts to fill, and go over what will happen the day of and a few days after surgery. It's different for every surgeon, so be sure to follow what your surgeon states.

The day before surgery

Date

◯ Complete any final preparations you were not able to get to in the couple of days before.

◯ Take out any of your metal jewelry, as you cannot wear metal of any kind during surgery. You can replace the metal jewelry with silicone or plastic jewelry, or with hole holders, so that the holes don't close.

◯ Your surgeon may request that you shower with a chlorhexidine skin cleanser, the same type the surgeon uses to wash their hands before an operation, the night before. These can be found at most local pharmacies under the brand name "Hibiclens", and they will give you instructions on how to use it.

◯ If having a vaginectomy, your surgeon may require you to stop eating midday, switching to a clear liquid diet, or to drink magnesium citrate to clear out your bowels.

◯ Stop eating and drinking anything by midnight.

The day of surgery, pre-op $\overline{\phantom{\text{Date}}}$
Date

◯ Do not eat or drink anything from midnight until after surgery.

Arrive at the surgery center, fill out any forms or necessary payment.

◯ Then you will be called to the back, where your surgeon and nurses will prep you for surgery. This usually includes getting into a hospital gown and hooking you up to saline and monitors.

◯ If you have not already had a hysterectomy, they may require you to do a pregnancy test, regardless of whether or not you have vaginal intercourse with someone who produces sperm.

◯ Your surgeon will later come in and discuss things to make sure you're still on the same page, and check in with you to see how you're feeling.

◯ Your anesthesiologist will come in and begin to set up, and potentially start, some of the anesthesia, and your surgical team will wheel you back to the operating room.

The day of surgery, post-op

◯ Meta generally takes 3-6 hours, depending on how complex your surgery is and how many aspects of surgery you are having done at the same time.

◯ When you wake up, you'll be in a recovery room with nurses who will bring you something to drink and potentially some easy-to-digest food like graham crackers, or pudding.

◯ You'll likely be groggy, going in and out of sleep, and will likely still feel woozy from the anesthesia.

◯ You may be naked from the waist down, or you may be in white, mesh underwear. Your surgical sites will be swaddled in gauze.

◯ If having UL, you will have a suprapubic (SP) catheter (a tube sticking out of the skin of your abdomen, halfway between your tdick and your belly button) that is draining your bladder. This stays in for around three weeks post-op. Some surgeons may also require that you have a "foley catheter" (a catheter through the urethra), though not all surgeons use both. You "pee" through these catheters, usually by having a bag that the catheter drains into strapped to your leg. Later, you will be given a valve to "pee" with in order to retrain your bladder.

◯ If not having UL, you may still have a foley catheter for a few days post-op to protect the surgical incisions from urine.

◯ Whether or not you stay in the hospital overnight depends on your surgeon, and your health insurance. In the US, overnight stays are uncommon, as most health insurances will not cover it for meta.

◯ Eventually, whoever is there for your recovery will be brought in to talk to you and bring you home.

The first 48 hours

◯ You will probably continue to feel woozy, with the haze of anesthesia hanging around for a few days post-op.

It will be painful to walk, and also painful to sit. Most people find that lying in a reclined position is the most comfortable position to be in.

It is mandatory that someone is with you after surgery to care for you, be responsible for your meds, or bring you back to the hospital if there are any severe complications (which can happen for any surgery).

Be sure to get up and walk around several times throughout the day, even if you don't want to. This helps prevent blood clots. You have a much higher risk of falling than you do in your day-to-day life, so you may want to walk arm-in-arm (getting additional balance) from the person there taking care of you.

It is expected that you won't be able to be very active and will tire easily. Be sure to give yourself the space you need to heal and rest as much as you need. You will spend most of this first week slowly recovering, drinking lots of water, and doing your best to keep your mind active.

The first week

Dates

Depending on your surgeon's instructions, you may change the bandages or clean your tdick with saline throughout the week before the post-op appointment, and you may be able to rinse your upper body (not getting any of the incisions wet), but all of this depends on your surgeon's instructions; every surgeon is different. Some surgeons will have you shower and remove bandages at 3 days post-op, while others want you to wait to get incisions wet until after the post-op appointment.

You will likely have difficulty wearing or putting on pants, both because of the locations of the incisions, as well as the suprapubic catheter (which rests right where the waistband of the pants usually is). Many people stay naked from the waist down for the first week post-op, when they can.

You'll have your first post-op appointment around 7 days post-op. They will check all of your incisions, ask you how you're feeling, and make sure there's nothing going on with the incisions or your recovery that they're worried about.

The first month

It continues to be painful to sit upright for 6-10 weeks post-op (depending on what combination of surgery you had), so most people continue to sit in a reclined position.

Around two weeks post-op, people start to move around a bit better, and get more frustrated with the SP catheter. Be sure to check in with yourself around this time, and give yourself grace for healing.

The second post-op appointment will be around 14 days post-op. At this point, the surgeon will again check all incisions, and give you a valve to replace the SP catheter bag. The valve allows you to retrain your bladder to hold urine.

After a few days of retraining your bladder with the valve, you are generally allowed to try to pee through your urethra. This can be hard to do, as you haven't actively peed in the last three weeks. Some people find getting in the shower and turning on warm water is helpful, while others find sitting on the toilet in the way they're used to can help with the "muscle memory" involved in the process.

It is expected for your urine stream to "spray" for the first few months post-op, due to swelling (think shower setting versus jet setting on a hose). As swelling goes down over the course of the next few months, your urine stream will slowly get more uniform.

Some surgeons may require a pee test, where they insert a dye ("contrast") into your bladder, then have you pee while they take x-ray images of it to visualize how well your new urethra is working. Not all surgeons require this.

Once you are successfully peeing out of your urethra, your surgeon removes your catheter, which is generally at 3 weeks post-op.

◯ Generally, you must stay in the area of your surgeon for 3 weeks post-op, though some surgeons will require less time. You will likely need to take at least 6 weeks off work, though you may need shorter off if you're working virtually, or longer off if you have a very physical job, complications, or your surgeon requests it.

The next few months
Dates

◯ It will likely continue to be painful to sit upright for a while.

◯ Your surgeon may ask you to "pump" in order to stop the incision's scarring from shortening your length (called "retraction"). Pumping is using a vacuum suction device to pull the tdick to its full length. This is generally begun at 6 weeks post-op, though it will depend on your surgeon. Pumping cannot be begun until all incisions are closed, and will likely reopen any scabbed over incisions or otherwise fragile tissue.

◯ Exercise can be begun around 8 weeks post-op, but only to the point that there is no pain or bleeding.

◯ Sexual activity is usually not allowed until 12 weeks post-op, though this varies by surgeon.

◯ If having UL without v-nectomy, some surgeons require you to "dilate," which is to use progressively larger plastic or silicone cylinders to "reopen" the vaginal entrance, and keep the scarring that you will have around the entrance pliable and supple.

Track Your Meds

Medication Name	Sunday AM	Sunday PM	Sunday Bed	Monday AM	Monday PM	Monday Bed	Tuesday AM	Tuesday PM	Tuesday Bed	Wednes-day AM	Wednes-day PM	Wednes-day Bed	Thurs-day AM	Thurs-day PM	Thurs-day Bed	Friday AM	Friday AM	Friday Bed	Saturday AM	Saturday PM	Saturday Bed

A letter to your post-op self

Sometimes after surgery, folks are hit with post-op depression, a tough mental place where they may question their decision or feel generally depressed. It comes from a variety of places, like having to limit your behavior, having complications, needing to have other people care for you, or your body having gone through trauma (no matter how necessary and important that trauma is). Use this space to write to your post-surgery self, as something you can read if you end up in that place. Some things you could write are: how important this is to you, to remember to take it slow, honoring your healing process, knowing how much better your life will be post-op, or whatever else feels right!

Phallo Timeline

What your phallo timeline looks like depends on what kind of phallo you're getting, how many stages your surgeon does it in, and what your surgeon separates into different stages. Because of that, this timeline will be a very general overview of what this may entail, though there are always options for differences.

As soon as you think you may be interested in phallo, call the offices of surgeons you may be interested in to book a consultation. Some of the more popular, well known surgeons are booking their consults 2-3 years in advance, with surgery another year after that.

Aside from prepping the donor site and removing any reproductive organs, it is essential to prep your body for surgery. Phalloplasty is a very intricate and complex surgery, and it's important to get your body and mind into a spot where you are ready for everything it entails, and any complications that may arise.

One year pre-op

Dates

◯ Begin performing any necessary hair removal from the donor site, if you are getting urethral lengthening. It takes somewhere between six months and a year of consistently attending weekly electrology appointments to kill enough hair follicles to be able to perform phallo, and one to two years to fully remove all hair from all hair cycles.

◯ Stop smoking, because nicotine limits healing abilities and may cause flap failure. Some surgeons require a blood test before surgery proving no nicotine usage.

◯ Improve your diet and overall health. Being active and eating in a way that is healthy for you will help your body to be as prepared as possible going into surgery.

◯ Prepare your mind so you are ready for any struggles or complications that may pop up. Some options are meditation, writing notes to yourself about how important this surgery is for you, finding friends who are going through or have gone through phallo, and going to therapy. Choose strategies that feel genuine to you.

6 months pre-op

◯ If you are getting a vaginectomy, have your reproductive organs removed 4-6 months beforehand. It is rare that a surgeon will allow these to be done in the same operation, as they are both complex procedures and will cause bleeding in similar areas.

◯ Make your travel plans.

◯ Complete any preparations that your surgeon may require of you.

The week before ⸻ Dates ⸻

◯ Gather any post-op supplies you will need and pack.

◯ Prepare your house/apartment so that anything you need will be on the first floor. Climbing stairs is very uncomfortable, and may not be possible for several days after being released from the hospital.

◯ If you are traveling to your surgeon, try to arrive a day before required, so your surgery is not potentially impacted or canceled by travel delays. Some surgeons may require an in-person pre-op appointment a day or two before your surgery, so ensure you're there in time.

◯ Attend a pre-op appointment, where they check in with you to make sure everything is okay, give you your medication scripts to fill, and go over what will happen the day of and a few days after surgery. It's different for every surgeon, so be sure to follow what your surgeon states.

The day before surgery ⸻ Date ⸻

◯ Complete any final preparations you were not able to get done in the couple of days before.

○ Take out any of your metal jewelry, as you cannot wear metal of any kind during surgery. You can replace the metal jewelry with silicone or plastic jewelry, or with hole holders, so that the holes don't close.

○ Your surgeon may request that you shower with a chlorhexidine skin cleanser, the same type the surgeon uses to wash their hands before an operation, the night before. These can be found at most local pharmacies under the brand name "Hibiclens", and they will give you instructions on how to use it.

○ If having a vaginectomy, your surgeon may require you to stop eating midday, switching to a clear liquid diet, and to drink magnesium citrate to clear out your bowels.

○ Stop eating and drinking anything by midnight.

The day of surgery, pre-op ⟨_____Date_____⟩

○ Do not eat or drink anything from midnight until after surgery.

○ Arrive at the surgery center, fill out any forms or necessary payment.

○ You will then be called to the back, where your surgeon and nurses will prep you for surgery. This usually includes getting into a hospital gown and hooking you up to saline and monitors.

○ If you have not already had a hysterectomy, they may require you to do a pregnancy test, regardless of whether or not you have vaginal intercourse with someone who produced sperm.

○ Your surgeon will come in and discuss things to make sure you're still on the same page, and check in with you to see how you're feeling. They may also draw on your donor site at this time.

Your anesthesiologist will come in and begin to set up, and potentially start, some of the anesthesia, and your surgical team will wheel you back to the operating room.

The day of surgery, post-op

Date

Phallo generally takes 6-12 hours, depending on how complex your surgery is and how many aspects of surgery you are having done at the same time.

When you wake up, you'll be in an ICU room with nurses who will check up on you every hour. You will stay in the ICU for ~3 days post-op, then move to a general inpatient room until 5-7 days post-op, after which you'll be discharged.

You are not allowed to eat or drink for ~24 hours post-op, in case you need to be brought back to the OR emergently.

You'll likely be groggy, going in and out of sleep, and will likely still feel woozy from the anesthesia.

You will be naked from the waist down, with your new dick propped up in a semi-erect position. This is to prevent the artery from kinking, which would cut off blood flow.

There will be a small light and series of wires attached to your new dick. This is colloquially called a "doppler," and will measure both the oxygenation of the blood in your new dick, as well as monitor the flow to make sure there's enough. In addition to the doppler being monitored by the ICU nurse, it is also often linked directly to your surgeon's cell phone. Should blood flow cease at any point, or oxygen saturation go down, it will send a notification to your surgeons, who will bring you back to the operating room to get blood flow back as soon as possible.

If having urethral lengthening, you will have a suprapubic (SP) catheter (a tube sticking out of the skin of your abdomen, halfway between your tdick and your belly button) that is draining your bladder. This stays in for at least three weeks post-op. Depending on your surgeon, you may also have a foley catheter (a catheter through the urethra), though not all surgeons use both. You "pee" through this, usually by having a bag that the catheter drains into strapped to your leg. Later, you will be given a valve to "pee" with in order to retrain your bladder.

◯ If not having urethral lengthening, you will have a foley catheter draining your bladder, which will usually be removed before you leave the hospital around day 5-7. This is to prevent you needing to get up to go to the bathroom.

◯ You will have a "vacuum dressing" on your donor site, helping the skin graft, or dermal matrix, adhere and heal.

◯ Depending on the rules of the hospital, you may be allowed visitors.

The first 48 hours
Date

◯ You will probably continue to feel woozy, with the haze of anesthesia hanging around for a few days post-op.

◯ Your surgeon may require that you do not walk or move around much during this time. Your bed may be remote controlled, allowing you to sit up to ~20°, but not much more, to avoid kinking the artery going to your new dick.

◯ Your nurse will be checking up on you and getting your vitals frequently. Anticipate being woken up every 1-2 hours, regardless of the time of day.

◯ If you are able to poop at this point, your nurse will assist you by helping you use a bedpan. It's semi-jokingly said that you should leave your dignity at the door, as your nurses will be helping with everything from pooping and wiping, to handling your new dick, to helping you walk.

◯ Your surgeon will likely check in on you each day, to make sure healing is going well.

The first week
Dates

◯ Around day three, your nurses may begin to help you get up and walk around several times throughout the day. This helps prevent blood clots. You have a much higher risk of falling, so they will likely help you by taking you arm-in-arm. At this point you will have been laying down for two or three whole days, so go slow, and take as much time as you need to let yourself adjust from laying down, to sitting up, to standing.

◯ It is expected that you won't be able to be very active and will tire easily. Be sure to give yourself the space you need to heal and rest as much as you need. You will spend most of this first week slowly recovering, drinking lots of water, and doing your best to keep your mind active.

◯ Depending on your surgeon's instructions, your bandages may be changed throughout this week.

◯ If you need or want to shower, your nurse will bathe you, usually with the assistance of another nurse, or a CNA (certified nursing assistant).

◯ You'll have your first official post-op appointment somewhere between 5-7 days post-op. At this post-op appointment, they will check on how all your healing is going, will likely remove the vacuum dressing and teach you how to do wound care on the donor site graft, and will discharge you from the hospital.

The first month

Dates

◯ You must continue to sit in a reclined position, as bending >90° may "kink" the artery feeding your new dick, in the same way that creating a kink in a hose blocks flow.

◯ It continues to be painful to sit fully upright for 6-10 weeks post-op, so most people continue to sit or lay in a reclined position.

◯ Around two weeks post-op, people start to move around a bit better, and many people get more frustrated with the healing process at this point. Be sure to check in with yourself around this time, and give yourself grace for healing.

◯ You must continue to prop your new dick up, in the same way as in the hospital. When standing or walking, most people either use a tool like "the donut" (a donut-shaped, thick foam support that holds your new dick "upright" when walking), "the cloud" (a series of gauze bandages that have been fluffed up and look cloud-like) or by holding their dick in their hand. When sitting, laying, or sleeping, most people either roll up gauze, or a spare set of underwear for their new dick to rest on, placing it behind their new dick.

☐ Wound care is done on the new dick itself, the site of the skin graft, and the donor site where the skin graft was applied. How this wound care is performed depends on your surgeon, so be sure to follow their recommendations.

☐ You are usually allowed to begin showering again, as long as you keep the donor site dry. Be sure to follow the surgeon's recommendations, as this may vary depending on technique and donor site.

☐ The second post-op appointment will be around 14 days after the initial surgery post-op. At this point, the surgeon will again check all sites from the surgery, and likely give you a valve to replace the SP catheter bag. The valve allows you to retrain your bladder to hold urine.

☐ After a few days of retraining your bladder with the valve, you are generally allowed to try to pee through your urethra. This can be hard to do, as you haven't actively peed in the last three weeks. Some people find getting in the shower and turning on warm water is helpful, while others find sitting on the toilet in the way they're used to can help with the "muscle memory" involved in the process.

☐ It is expected for your urine stream to "spray" for the first few months post-op, due to swelling (think shower setting versus jet setting on a hose). As swelling goes down over the course of the next few months, your urine stream will slowly get more uniform.

☐ Some surgeons may require a pee test, where they insert a dye ("contrast") into your bladder, then have you pee while they take x-ray images of it to visualize how well your new urethra is working. Not all surgeons require this.

Once you are successfully peeing out of your urethra, your surgeon removes your catheter, which is generally 3 weeks post-op.

If you had a dermal matrix (like integra) placed, you may have a small second surgery at 2-3 weeks post-op to place the skin graft atop this matrix. Follow-up care for this varies, so follow the directions of your surgeon.

Generally, you must stay in the area of your surgeon for an absolute minimum of 3 weeks post-op, though some surgeons will require more time. You will likely need to take at least 6 weeks off work if it is remote, though you may need longer off if you have a very physical job, complications, or your surgeon requests it.

Depending on the location of the donor site, you may begin doing physical therapy to regain strength and dexterity around two weeks post-op.

The next few months

Dates

It will likely continue to be painful to sit upright for a while.

You will be required to keep your new dick "propped" for ~8-12 weeks post-op, depending on your surgeon and donor site.

Light exercise can begin around 8 weeks post-op, but only to the point where there is no pain or bleeding. People are generally released to "full activity" at 12 weeks post-op, but this may differ depending on personal healing.

Sexual activity is usually not allowed until 12 weeks post-op, at a minimum, though this varies by surgeon.

In order to soften and improve healing of the donor site, many people use silicone, either in the form of silicone sheets or silicone sleeves that can be slid over the donor site.

Try not to expose your donor site to the sun, as this can irreversibly alter the coloring of it, as well as potentially impact flexibility and pliability.

Track Your Meds

Medication Name	Sunday AM	Sunday PM	Sunday Bed	Monday AM	Monday PM	Monday Bed	Tuesday AM	Tuesday PM	Tuesday Bed	Wednes-day AM	Wednes-day PM	Wednes-day Bed	Thurs-day AM	Thurs-day PM	Thurs-day Bed	Friday AM	Friday AM	Friday Bed	Saturday AM	Saturday PM	Saturday Bed

A letter to your post-op self

Sometimes after surgery, folks are hit with post-op depression, a tough mental place where they may question their decision or feel generally depressed. It comes from a variety of places, like having to limit your behavior, having complications, needing to have other people care for you, or your body having gone through trauma (no matter how necessary and important that trauma is). Use this space to write to your post-surgery self, as something you can read if you end up in that place. Some things you could write are: how important this is to you, to remember to take it slow, honoring your healing process, knowing how much better your life will be post-op, or whatever else feels right!

OTHER ASPECTS OF PHYSICAL TRANSITION

In addition to everything listed above, there are also other options and routes that are possible. Most often, these are effects that you would have from testosterone but that you may need to supplement if the testosterone has not had the effect on your body that you wanted, or if you do not want to take (or cannot take) testosterone for any reason. Here is space to write down your thoughts and feelings about pursuing them.

Vocal Therapy (for a deeper voice)

Voice Deepening Surgery

Body Masculinization Surgery

Minoxidil (for facial hair growth)

Finasteride (for stopping hair growth)

DHT Cream (for bottom growth)

Compound Cream (for bottom growth)

RESOURCES

You don't need to undertake this process alone! Here are places that can be helpful with finding community, financial, and mental health support.

Community

It is always important to have support and understanding in your life. I will always recommend finding and participating in transgender or LGBT+ groups in your area, as this can be a safe space to explore yourself, your transition, your wants and needs, and to ask people about their personal experiences. Some good places to look for or find local support groups are:

- Google Searches

- Local LGBT (or Queer) Resource Centers

- QSA or GSA groups in your highschool, or LGBT resource centers at your college, if you are in school

- Autostraddle's Queer Guide to your city, if you live in a larger city

- Finding one other trans or queer person will often connect you with a collection of fellow LGBT+ people, who in turn will have their own groups of friends or resources

- Asking in the Facebook groups below

If you don't have the ability to participate in groups in your area, or they don't exist, below is a list of Facebook groups that you can join. It should be noted, all of the groups below *are* nonbinary friendly, and all of them have rules about blocking people for being medical exclusionists. I am not a moderator in these groups, and can only recommend them based off of how I've seen the groups act in the past.

Facebook groups:

- Nonbinary physical transition discussion

- Non Binary Physical Transition Discussion
- FTM/NB/GNC Testosterone
- Testosterone Bottom Growth and Sexual Health Support Group
- Top Surgery Support (Removal/Reduction)
- Non-Binary Top Surgery
- I have no nipples (or may not have nipples in the future)
- Inclusive Trans Mascs and Where to Find Them
- Transgender Shitposting Selfies and Support
- Trans Men, Masc + NB Ireland
- You can also ask in any of the above groups for access to bottom surgery groups. Most of them are secret groups, so you will not be able to find them by searching for them, only by being added by a person who is already a member.

There are often great groups on other forms of social media like reddit, discord, instagram, tumblr, and more. You could find them by asking in some of the Facebook groups above, googling topics you're curious about with associated keywords, or using the search function on any social media's particular website.

Binders

If you are in need of a binder but cannot afford one yourself, these companies offer used, discounted, or free binders:

- Point of Pride
- Big Brothers Binder Program
- The Binder Project
- FTM Essentials (for trans youth only, age 24 or under)

- MORF Binder Scheme

- QMunity

- Come as You Are Cooperative

- Trans Social Media Groups

- Your local LGBT resource center

- Friends who may no longer be using their binders

- Companies like gc2b also frequently do sales during pride month

Paying for Surgery

Because surgery is exceedingly expensive, and often US insurance won't cover it or there may be issues getting coverage in countries like the UK or Ireland that are medically exclusionary (unless you're doing what they determine a "full transition" to a binary gender, they won't give you coverage for treatment), below is a list of scholarship organizations who you can apply to for assistance paying for surgeries:

- Point of Pride

- Genderbands

- Jim Collins Foundation

- Flavnt

- CK Life

- Rizi Xavier Timane Surgery Grant

- Local Resources

Mental Health Support

If you need mental health support, these are resources are specifically for the trans and queer community.

- Trans Lifeline: +1 (877) 565-8860 *www.translifeline. org*

- Organized and run by all trans volunteers, you can call this line at any hour of the day to talk with other trans people.

- Trevor Project: +1 (866) 488-7386 *www.thetrevorproject.org*

  - A hotline of trained counselors available at all hours of the day, to call if you are in crisis or just need a safe and judgment-free zone to call.

- It Gets Better Project: *www.itgetsbetterproject.org*

  - A resource with a compilation of videos from LGBT+ people all over the globe. You can watch videos and stories of people's experiences, and how It Gets Better.

- Trans Family Support Services (Trans SOS): *transfamilysos.org*

  - A resource to assist both families and individual trans people in getting access to resources.

More Resources

Any other resources or information you've found that you want to keep track of? Write them down here:

CONCLUSION

Overall, how you decide to physically transition is up to you. It's up to your wants, your needs, your feelings, and your desires. No one can make these decisions for you, and I highly recommend taking the time to think through all the options and questions available.

Remember, no matter what options you choose, who you are, your gender, and your identity are not any less valid for choosing or not choosing different options. Who you are becoming, and taking the time to find yourself, is what is important.

Now that you've read and worked through all or parts of this book, check in with yourself again. What are your reflections and thoughts on physical transition going forward? What questions do you still have?

Notes

Notes

Notes

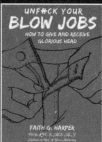